Jonah and the Big Fish

Written by Katherine Sully
Illustrated by Simona Sanfilippo

QED Publishing

Most of the time, Jonah was a good man.

So one day, God asked Jonah to do a job for him.

"Go to the city of Nineveh, and deliver a message for me."

But Jonah didn't want to go to Nineveh.
Instead he ran away.

Jonah found a boat to take him far away from Nineveh.
He hid below deck and fell fast asleep.

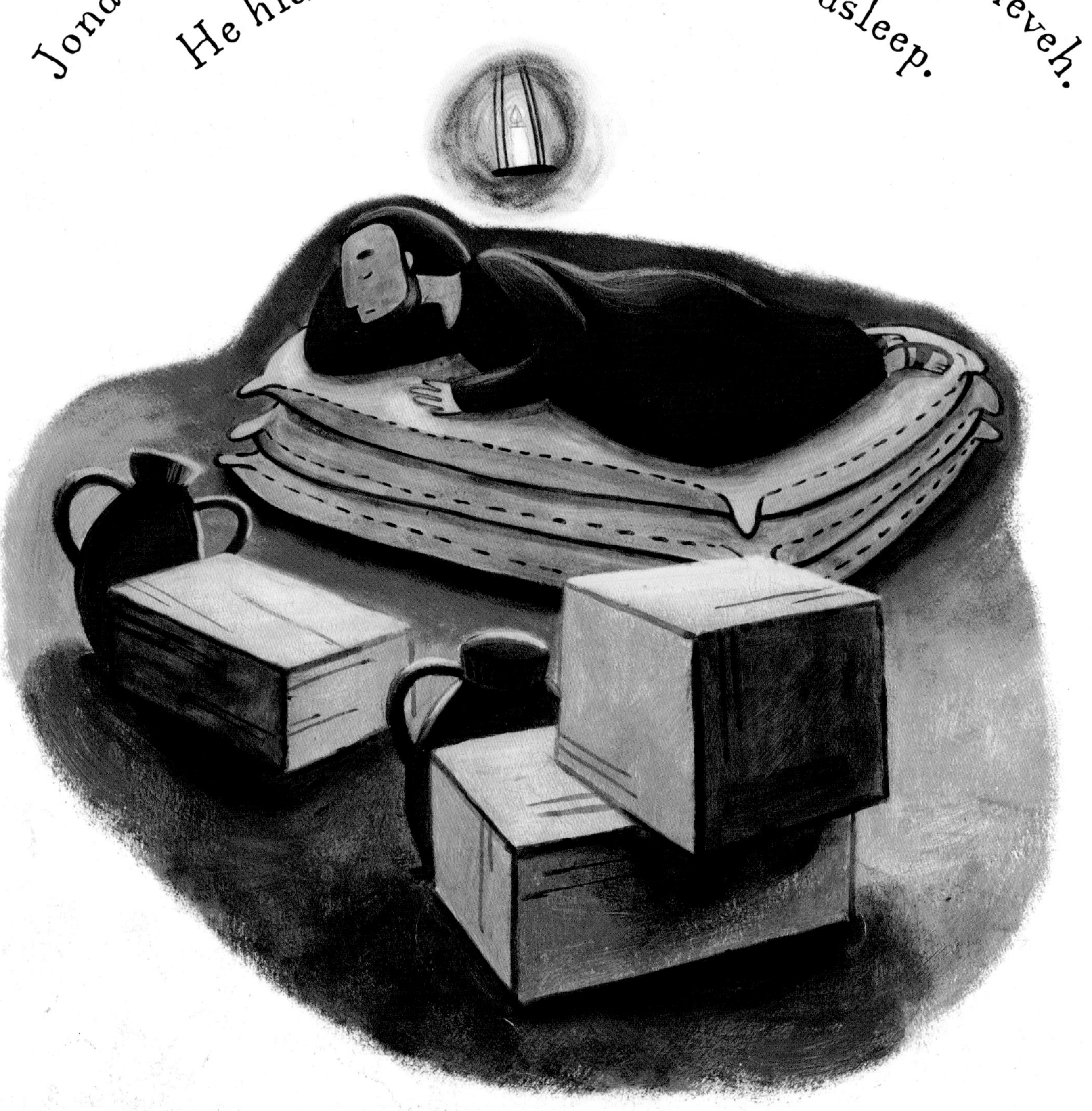

As he slept, the wind blew and the waves crashed.

A storm rocked the boat and still Jonah slept!

The captain of the boat came to wake Jonah.

"How can you sleep in this storm!"
cried the captain.
"Get up and say a prayer!"

The boat rocked this way and that way.
The sailors were all afraid.
"Tip the cargo overboard!"
the captain cried.

But it was no use. The storm grew wilder and wilder.
"It's my fault," said Jonah. "I didn't do as God asked me."
The sailors were shocked and afraid.

"God is angry with me," said Jonah.
"Tip me overboard and the storm will stop."

Now the sailors didn't really want to tip Jonah overboard. They prayed and prayed. But still the storm rocked the boat.

Finally, they tipped Jonah SPLOSH! into the waves.

SPLOSH!

And the storm stopped!

Jonah sank through the water

deeper

and

deeper.

Jonah began to pray:
"I'm sinking down!
Don't let me drown!"

Then he saw a great big fish swim towards him.
The fish opened its mouth wide, wider –
and swallowed him
in one gulp.
GULP!

Jonah sat inside the fish's belly.
He had plenty of time to think. He had run
away from God and was punished.

He had prayed to God
and was saved. Now Jonah thanked
God and God forgave him.

After three days, the big fish burped.
Jonah shot out of its mouth and landed on a beach!

This time, Jonah went to the city of Nineveh to deliver God's message.

The people there were wicked. They didn't listen to God either.

For three days Jonah walked
through the city, calling,
"Mend your ways in forty days
or Nineveh will be destroyed!"

When they heard Jonah's message from God, the people of Nineveh were shocked.

Even the King of Nineveh was shocked.

They had forgotten that God was watching them.

They were very sorry that they had been bad and decided to be good from then on.

So God forgave them.

Jonah sat on a hill outside Nineveh and waited for the city to be destroyed.

But it was very hot and nothing happened. Jonah became very grumpy.

God said to Jonah,
“Why are you grumpy?
I forgave you because I
love you. I forgave the
people of Nineveh
because I love them.”
And finally Jonah understood that
God’s love was big enough for everyone.

Next Steps

Look back through the book to find more to talk about and join in with.

* Copy the actions. Pretend you are in a boat being tossed by the waves. Pretend you are a fish. Make a wave action with your hand and arm.
* Join in with the rhyme. Pause to encourage joining in with 'I'm sinking down! Don't let me drown!'
* Count the days. Jonah is inside the big fish for three days. Nineveh has 40 days to mend its way. Talk about how long three days is and how long 40 days is.
* Name the colours of the fish together, then look back to spot the colours on other pages.
* Find shapes and sizes. Compare the big fish with the other fishes on the page.
* How big is the big fish compared with the boat?
* Listen to the sounds. When you see the word on the page, point and make the sound – Splosh! Gulp!

Now that you've read the story... what do you remember?

* Who was Jonah?
* Why did he run away to sea?
* Where did Jonah end up when he was tipped into the sea?
* How did Jonah get out of the big fish?
* What happened when Jonah got to Nineveh?
* Why did Jonah become grumpy?

What does the story tell us?
If we do the wrong thing, God will show us the right thing to do.

For Antony.

First published in hardback in 2011 by Hodder Children's Books
Paperback edition published in 2012

Hodder Children's Books
338 Euston Road
London NW1 3BH

Hodder Children's Books Australia
Level 17/207 Kent Street
Sydney NSW 2000

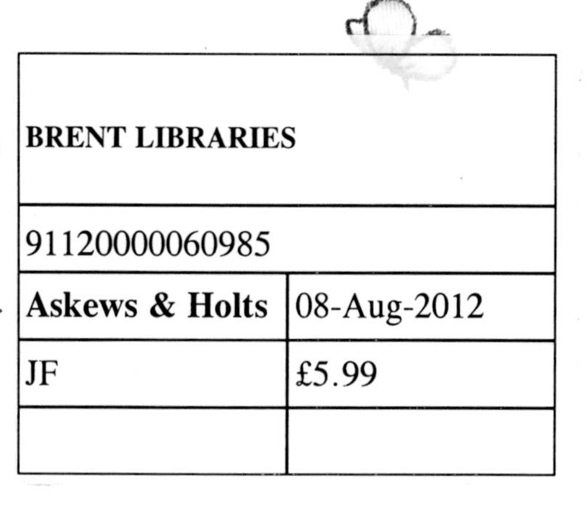

A catalogue record of this book is available from the British Library.

ISBN: 978 0 340 99944 8

10 9 8 7 6 5 4 3 2 1

Printed in China

Hodder Children's Books is a division
of Hachette Children's Books.
An Hachette UK Company

www.hachette.co.uk

MICHAEL
BROAD

Hodder
Children's
Books

A division of Hachette Children's Books

SEARCHING FOR LUSH GREEN PASTURES, the herd joined the other animals moving towards the distant mountains. Everyone was tired and hungry.

Only one young elephant was keen to make new friends.

‘Can I go and play, Mama?’ asked Forget-Me-Not, seeing some warthogs having fun.

‘Yes, my darling,’ smiled his mother. ‘But play nicely with the little ones.’

'I will,' he promised and hurried over to join them.

But not all of the warthogs were having fun. The littlest one looked very sad indeed.

Her brothers were calling her names.

'Big snout,' snorted one.

'Scruffy bristles,' sniffed another.

'Teeny-tiny, ugly-wugly!' they all jeered.

'My mama says to play nicely with the little ones,' said Forget-Me-Not bravely. 'And teasing someone small is not very nice at all.'

'Then **you** can play with her!'
grunted the warthogs
as they scampered away.

‘I’m Forget-Me-Not,’ said the young elephant, kindly.

‘What’s your name?’

'I'm Buttercup,' said the shy little warthog.
'But everyone calls me Ugly.'

'I don't think you're ugly,' said Forget-Me-Not and he played with his new friend all day long.

The hyenas laughed at how little Buttercup was.
But Forget-Me-Not ignored them.

Being small meant that she was very
good at playing hide-and-seek.

He took no notice of the reed frogs when they chuckled at Buttercup's long, scruffy bristles.

They were just right for tickling his trunk,
which always made him giggle.

And when the ostriches squawked at Buttercup's big snout,
she used it to nudge a ball between their spindly legs.

Then Forget-Me-Not chased after her, which made the ostriches squawk even louder!

'Everyone is unkind to Buttercup because of the way she looks,' said Forget-Me-Not as he cuddled next to his mama that evening. 'But I think she's beautiful.'

'That's because you see what's on the inside,' said his mother. 'One day, the others will see it, too.'

'And then they'll know how special she is?' asked Forget-Me-Not, hopefully.

'With a friend like you, I'm certain they will,' she said and stroked the little elephant's head until he fell fast asleep.

The following day, the animals reached the mountains. But no one knew which path led to the lush green pastures.

The hyenas were silent.
The reed frogs hid beneath their parasols.
And the ostriches buried their heads in the sand.

'I think I can help,' said Buttercup and she whispered into Forget-Me-Not's ear.

'Buttercup can find the way!' cried Forget-Me-Not.

'Ugly can't possibly help us,' scoffed the other animals.

But she did. Little Buttercup's big snout could smell the sweet grass and the scent of her favourite flowers. Her long bristles felt the slight cool breeze.

And she was small enough to stand on Forget-Me-Not's back and lead everyone through the mountains.

Soon the animals reached the lush green pastures full of bright yellow buttercups. They looked at the little warthog gratefully. She had wanted to help everyone even after they were mean to her.

And suddenly they saw what Forget-Me-Not had known all along. Buttercup was truly beautiful.

Wish upon Forget-Me-Not's buttercups to see the beauty inside everyone.

More wonderful adventures of

Forget-Me-Not

the little elephant

and his friends.